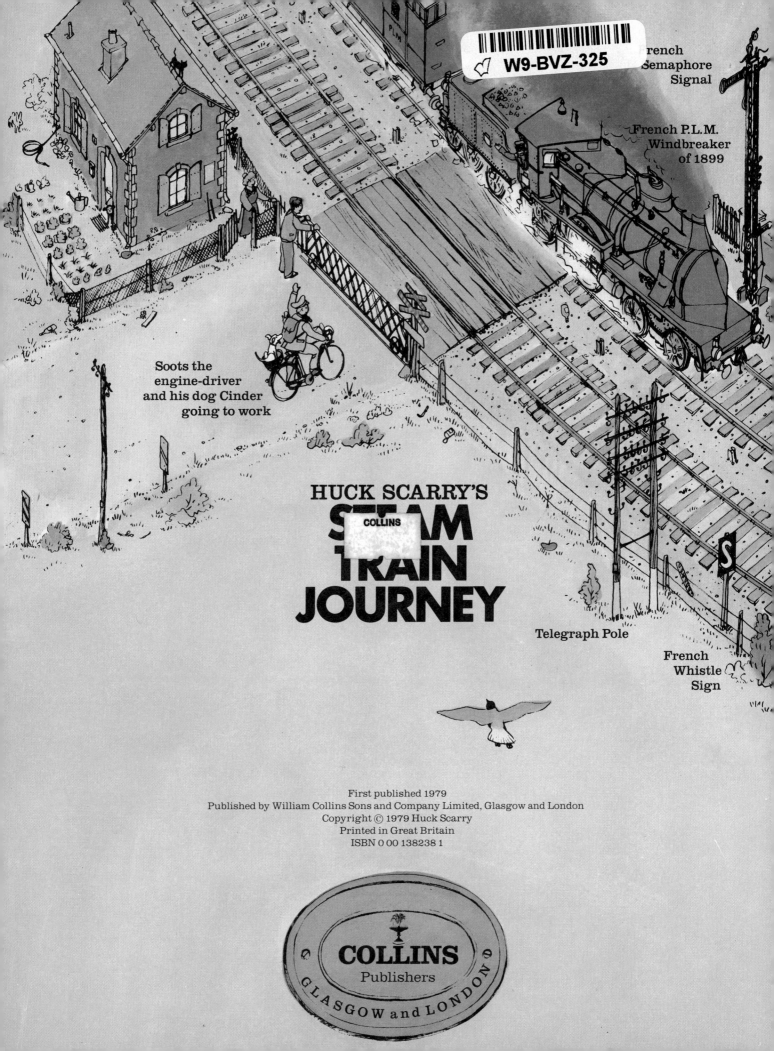

French Semaphore Signal

French P.L.M. Windbreaker of 1899

Soots the engine-driver and his dog Cinder going to work

HUCK SCARRY'S
STEAM TRAIN JOURNEY

Telegraph Pole

French Whistle Sign

First published 1979
Published by William Collins Sons and Company Limited, Glasgow and London
Copyright © 1979 Huck Scarry
Printed in Great Britain
ISBN 0 00 138238 1

COLLINS
Publishers
GLASGOW and LONDON

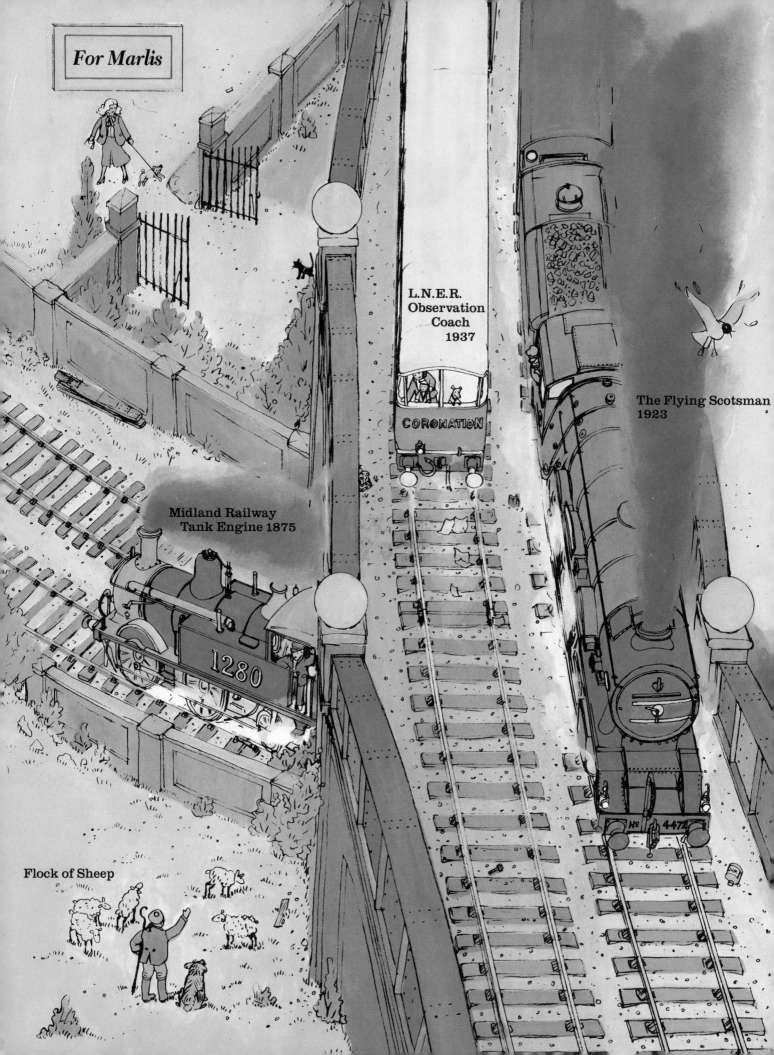

For Marlis

Midland Railway
Tank Engine 1875

1280

L.N.E.R.
Observation
Coach
1937

CORONATION

The Flying Scotsman
1923

N° 4472

Flock of Sheep

Let's jump aboard with Soots and his dog Cinder as they take their steam train on an imaginary journey and see the old trains of many lands...

BEFORE the sun is up, Soots the engine driver and Cinder his dog cycle to the engine shed where their locomotive is waiting to take them on the day's journey.

Sparks the fireman is getting up steam in the boiler of Soots' engine.

Engine Shed

Great Western Railway Tank Engine

Midland Railway Mail Coach
picking up mail at speed

Gradient Sign

Roundhouse

Hayes Ten-Wheeler,
Baltimore and Ohio
Railroad 1853

American Baggage Car

NEW YORK CENTRAL

SOOTS drives out of the shed and onto the
turntable that will put his engine on the
right lines.
   An express train shoots by and Soots gives
a friendly wave.

Turntable

New York Central Railroad No. 999, the world's fastest locomotive in 1895

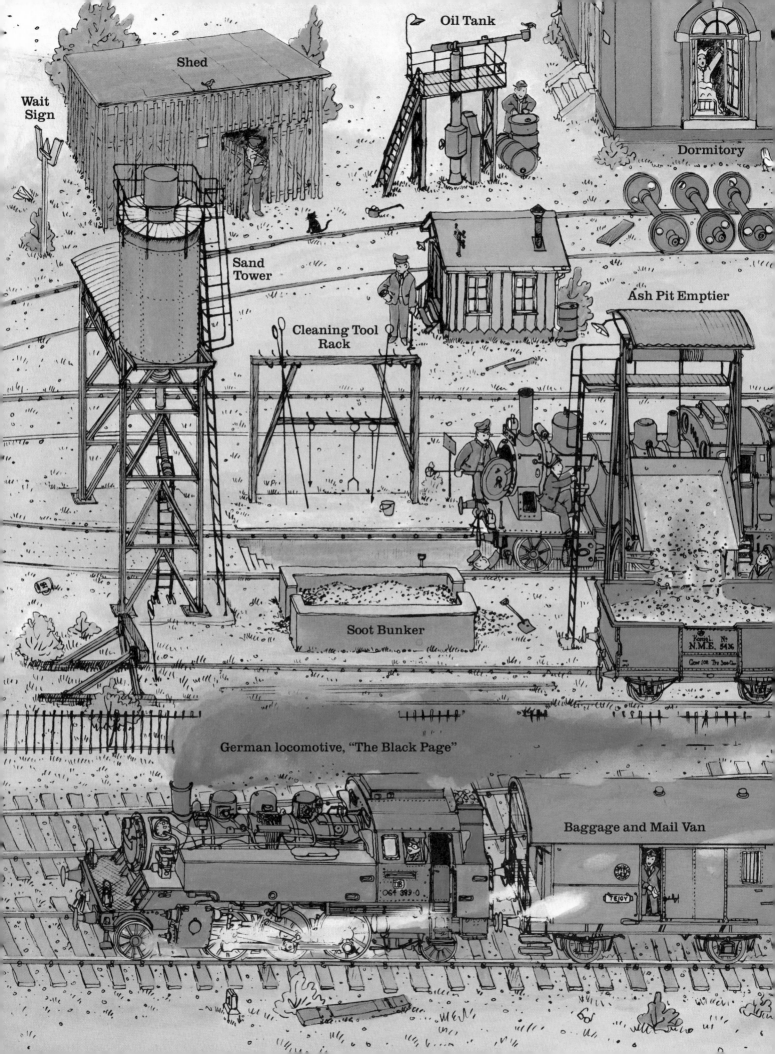

Wait Sign

Shed

Oil Tank

Dormitory

Sand Tower

Cleaning Tool Rack

Ash Pit Emptier

Soot Bunker

German locomotive, "The Black Page"

Baggage and Mail Van

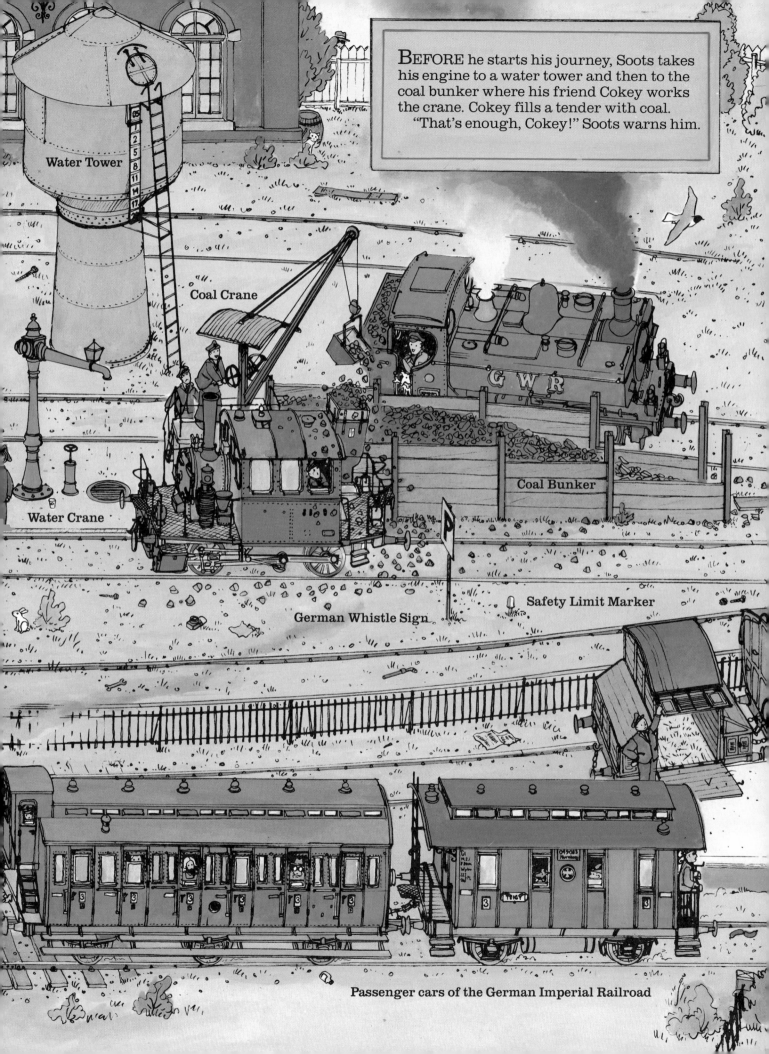

BEFORE he starts his journey, Soots takes his engine to a water tower and then to the coal bunker where his friend Cokey works the crane. Cokey fills a tender with coal. "That's enough, Cokey!" Soots warns him.

Water Tower

Coal Crane

Water Crane

Coal Bunker

German Whistle Sign

Safety Limit Marker

Passenger cars of the German Imperial Railroad

WITH a full head of steam, Soots drives his engine across the points to the station. Here the engine is coupled to carriages waiting at the platform.

Tourist

Platform

Great Western Railway carriage for local train

Footbridge

Coupler

Passengers boarding train

THE passengers clamber on board, and Oates the horse is led to his special wagon. The whistle blows and the train chugs off on its journey.

Lavatories

Clock

Station-master

Bench

Great Western Railway Diesel Railcar 1934

Luggage

Lamp Repairman

Odometer

Great Western Railway Dynamometer Car of 1903, which measures speed and performance of locomotives

JUST out of the station Soots passes the
signal box. That is where the points and
signals operate to keep the train on the
right track.

In the goods siding, freight is being loaded
onto special wagons.

Goods Station

Loading Platform

Ramp

Crane

Grain Wagon

Cattle Box

Open Brick Wagon

Route Indicator

Block Instruments showing train positions

SIGNAL LEVER   LOCK LEVER   SWITCH LEVER

London, Midland and Scottish Railway Signal Box

Point Lever Mechanism

Semaphore Signal

Point Mechanism

Covered Wagon

NORTH EASTERN
102490

L.N.E.R. Tank Locomotive
(ex N.E.R. 1898)

L N E R
580

GWR

FIRST   THIRD

Sleeping Tramp

Great Northern Railway Well Wagon
carrying Vulcan Tank Locomotive (the first engine
in Japan, 1871)

THE little train puffs uphill and into a tunnel where it disappears from sight.
"Keep your head in, Oates, or you'll surely lose it!"

English Horse Box

Swiss Distant Signal

Imperial Austrian Railway Express Locomotive

Gradient Sign

Swiss Whistle Sign

Swiss Rotary Snowplough (a converted steam locomotive)

Swiss locomotive which runs on compressed air, used during tunnel construction

Tunnel Portal
(St Gotthard Tunnel)

Cut stones for
tunnel building

Measuring Instruments

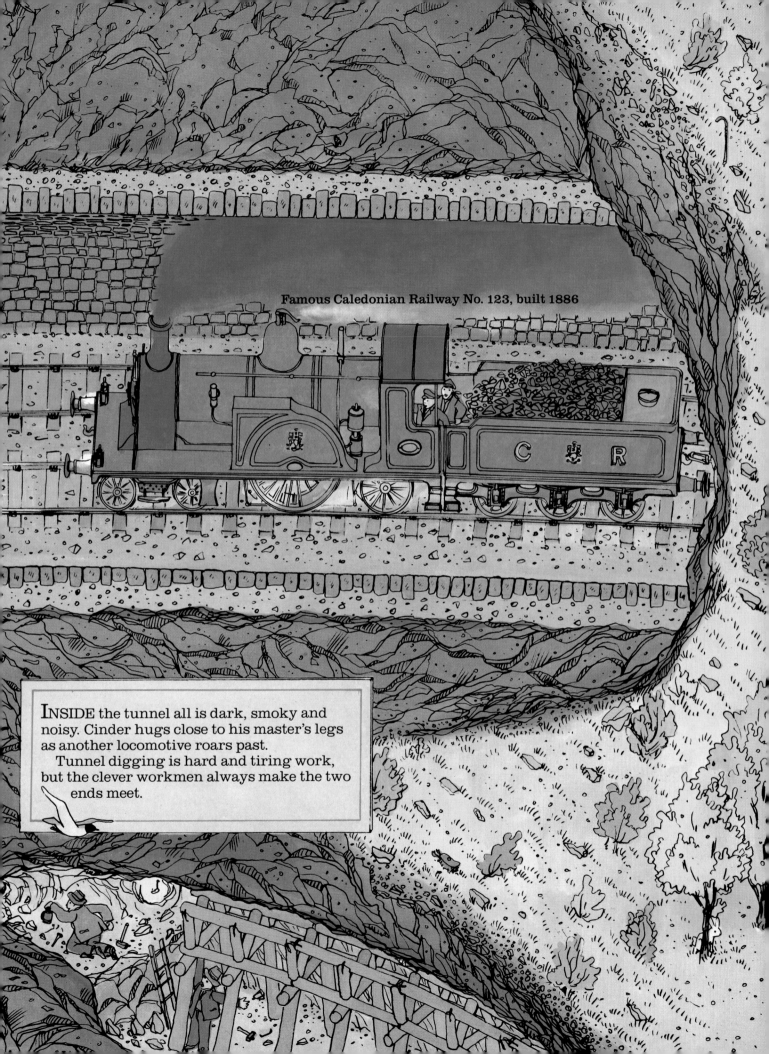

Famous Caledonian Railway No. 123, built 1886

INSIDE the tunnel all is dark, smoky and
noisy. Cinder hugs close to his master's legs
as another locomotive roars past.
  Tunnel digging is hard and tiring work,
but the clever workmen always make the two
ends meet.

SOOTS stops the train at a small station. Some passengers get off and some new passengers climb aboard. While he is waiting for the whistle, Soots waves to some people passing swiftly by in an observation carriage.

Station Name Sign

RUNNING-on-TYME

Tail Steering Cab

Scammell 100-ton tractor of 1929, carrying an Australian locomotive of the New South Wales Railway 186

Old Great Western Railway
Station 1848

Leyland Lion Bus 1929

Great Western Railway
Scammell
Truck 1937

Caledonian Railway
Observation Car

PULLMAN

Footbridge

British
Whistle Sign

Driver's Cab

Life-belt

SOOTS steams out of the station and over the drawbridge. Oates looks back to see the bridge go up into the air to let Captain Saltspray's trawler pass underneath.
    Look at the fisherman! I hope he can swim!

Hamburg Harbour Police
Steam Launch 1900

German Steam Trawler
1907

Bridge
Control Cab

Motor

Balance Weight

3-ton Crane

Netherlands Central Railways Express Locomotive "the Zeppelin," 1910

AT the dockside a crane is lifting bananas from the hold of a barge into a railway wagon.

Who is that cheeky monkey eating the bananas?

Dutch Tank Locomotive of 1930

Netherlands Central Railways 2nd Class Coach, 1900

French Articulated
Freight Locomotive

French Box Car with Brakeman's cab,
built in America during World War I

French Box Car for carrying vegetables,
also used to carry 8 horses or 60 uncomfortable men

French Diesel Railcar
on rubber tyres, 1931

French Rotating Stop Signal

GRAND FE

French Locomotive
which pulled the first Orient Express
in 1883

French Flatcar

erman
oultry Wagon

French Brakeman's Van

General Motors Truck,
converted to run
on rails,
World War II

As the train slows down Oates sees in the
sidings lots of wagons and engines waiting
to be made up into trains. Over on another
line a railcar rolls along quietly on its
rubber wheels.

ALLEY

French
Baggage Van

Smoke
Roof

DES WAGONS-LITS

SLEEPING CAR

950

490   490

THIRD   SECOND   FIRST   THIRD

Station Inspector   Personnel Locker-room

THE railway tracks lead into a large building. Soots' train has reached the terminus, the end of the line. He pulls on the brake and with a last hiss the engine comes to a halt.

CE INTERNATIONALE DES WAGONS-LITS.

1867 French Sleeping Car

WAGON-LITS

SLEEPING CAR

Sleepwalker

1873 Austrian Sleeping Car

SCHLAF-WAGEN COMPAGNE INTERNATIONALE DES WAGONS-LITS SLEEPING CAR

GWR

WELCOME

Lost and Found

Left Luggage

Post Office

Time-Table

Flowers

Controller

Tickets

Waiting Rooms

1922 Foden
Steam Bus

Jockey

1907
Stanley
Steamer

THE passengers get off. So do Soots and
Cinder. Soots buys some flowers to give to his
girl friend, Ashlie.
    Cinder gives Ashlie's dog Cinderella a very
large but very black bone.
    Soots is off to have a bath. Cinder too is
going to wash and it is time for us to wave
them goodbye!